W9-CGP-720

HATS AND BEARS

Florence Parry Heide
Sylvia Worth Van Clief

Senior Authors
Carl B. Smith
Ronald Wardhaugh

Macmillan Publishing Co., Inc.
New York

Collier Macmillan Publishers
London

SERIES r™
Macmillan Reading

Copyright © 1980 Macmillan Publishing Co., Inc.

All rights reserved. No part of this book may be reproduced or transmitted in any form or by any means, electronic or mechanical, including photocopying, recording, or by any information storage and retrieval system, without permission in writing from the Publisher.

ACKNOWLEDGMENTS

Illustrations: Ray Cruz, pp. 2-3; Errol LeCain, pp. 4-17; Marty Norman, pp. 18-19; Linda Gist, pp. 20-45; Joanne Scribner, pp. 46-47; Lionel Kalish, pp. 48-49. **Cover Design:** AKM Associates

Parts of this work were published in SERIES ſ: The New Macmillan Reading Program.

Macmillan Publishing Co., Inc.
866 Third Avenue, New York, New York 10022
Collier Macmillan Canada, Ltd.

Printed in the United States of America
ISBN 0-02-128270-6
9876543

Contents

THINGS

Suzy paints a house.

"I don't like that.
It looks funny,"
says Bob.

"I like to paint funny things,"
says Suzy.

Suzy paints a pony
on the house.

"I don't like it.
It looks funny to see a pony
on a house,"
says Bob.

"I like funny things,"
says Suzy.

9

Suzy paints a fish
on the pony.

"I don't like it.
It looks funny to see a fish
on a pony,"
says Bob.

"I like funny things,"
says Suzy.

11

"A fish can't live
on a pony," says Bob.
"A fish likes to live
in a lake."
"A pony can't run
on a house," says Bob.
"A pony likes to run
in a park."

"I like funny things,"
says Suzy.

"I don't,"
says Bob.

13

Bob paints a house.
He paints a pony
in a park.
He paints a fish
in a lake.

14

Suzy sees the house,
the pony, and the fish.

"I don't like your house,
your pony, or your fish,"
says Suzy.
"I like funny things."

16

Standing in Line

Standing in line,
Standing in line,
Someone's ahead of me
Every time.
Someone's ahead
And someone's behind
Every time I'm standing in line!

20

Hats and Hats

Part One

Funny Hats

I like your hat.
You have funny hats.

23

25

Part Two
In and Out

We like your house.
And we like you.
May we come in?

28

I like hats.
And I like you.
Come in.

31

33

34

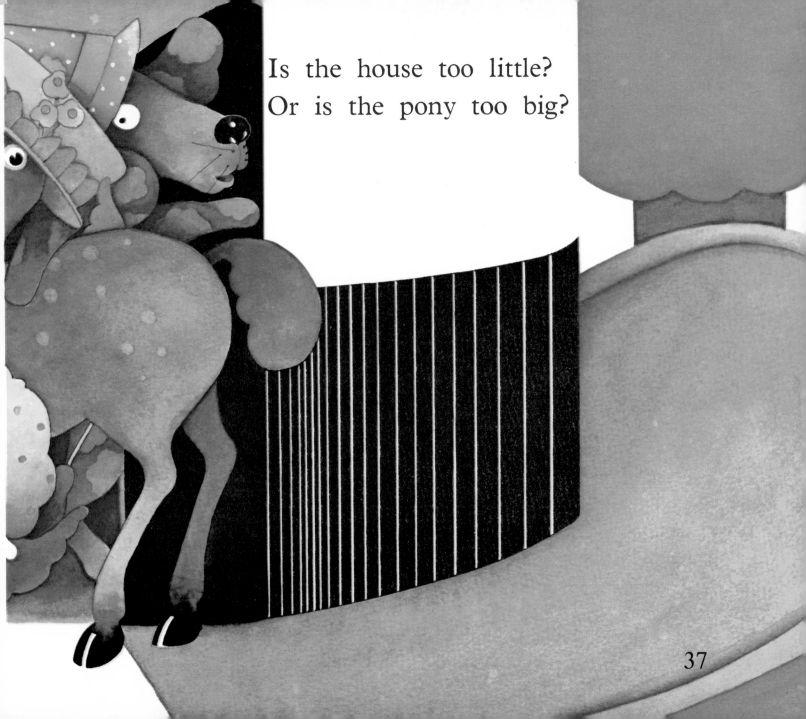

Is the house too little?
Or is the pony too big?

37

I like the house.
I like the house that is a hat.
But I like the pony, too.

38

41

That house is too little.
We will go to the city.
We will live in a big house
in the city.

We like the house.
We like the house that is a hat.

45

HAT
ON MY
HEAD

Hat on my head,
Shoes on my feet,
That is the best way I've found.
I know it's true
Because I've tried
The other way around.

What Did You Say?

"Where are the dogs?"

"The dogs are in the park."

1. Kim says, "We will go to the park."
2. Bob says, "We can go on the bus."
3. "Do you see the dogs?" says Kim.
4. "The dogs are lost," says Bob.
5. Kim says, "I will call the dogs."
6. "I see the dogs!" says Bob.

BIG BEAR

51

Part One
Ben

Ben is a bear.
Ben is a big bear.
He likes to run
and jump.

52

Ben runs to the boys
and girls.
But then the boys and girls
run home.

Ben is sad.
Why is he sad?
The boys and girls
don't like Ben.

54

"Boys and girls can read,"
says Ben.
"I can read, too.
Then I can read
with the boys and girls.
Then I can run and jump
with the boys and girls."

55

But the boys and girls
don't read with Ben.
The boys and girls
run home.

56

Part Two
The Party

The boys and girls
have a party.

"Boys and girls like
presents," Ben says.
"I have a present.
I can come to the party.
The boys and girls
will like the present.
Then the boys and girls
will like me."

57

Ben does have a present.
But the boys and girls
don't like Ben.

58

Ben sits.
And Ben sits.
He is sad.
"The boys and girls
don't like me,"
he says.
Then it rains.
It rains and rains.

Ben looks at the present.
What is it?
What is the present?
The present is
a big umbrella.

60

It rains and rains.
It rains
on the boys and girls.
It rains on the umbrella.

61

The boys and girls see Ben
and the umbrella.
The boys and girls run.

The boys and girls run
to Ben and the umbrella.
The boys and girls have
a party with Ben.
The boys and girls like Ben.

Ben says,
"I like the boys and girls,
and the boys and girls like me!"

WORD LIST

7. Suzy	26. *lives*	52. Ben
paints	27. may	53. then
don't	28. come	54. sad
it	30. at	55. with
looks	38. three	57. party
paint	39. will	presents
8. on	country	*present*
21. hats	40. red	me
22. *hat*	48. did	59. rains
have	say	60. umbrella
	50. bear	

To the Teacher: The words listed beside the page numbers above are introduced in *Hats and Bears*, Level 6 of SERIES r. The children should be able to use previously taught skills to identify the italicized words independently.